Dipper to the rescue

Written by Monica Hughes

Illustrated by Robert McPhillips

Dipper was a dolphin.
She was happy in the sea.
One day Dipper swam up and over
some big waves.

Then Dipper saw a man.
The man was on a sailboard.
He could go up and over the waves,
just like Dipper.

Dipper swam over to the man.
They went up and over the big waves.
They were very happy.

Then the wind blew.

It blew and blew and blew.

The waves got very big.

Dipper was happy in the
very big waves.
But the man was not happy.
The waves were too big for him.

The man fell off his sailboard.
Dipper swam over to the man
and tried to help him.

The man went down and down
into the sea.
Dipper tried and tried but she
could not help him.

Then the man fell on a rock.
Dipper swam down to help him.

The man put his arms on Dipper.
Then he put his legs on her back.

Dipper and the man went up and up.
Then they went over the waves
and on to the sand.

Dipper put the man down on the sand.
The man was happy.
So was Dipper and she swam off
over the sea.

And she got the sailboard!